CHRISTOPHER NORTON

microlatin

20 new pieces based on
LATIN-AMERICAN rhythms
for the BEGINNER
to INTERMEDIATE pianist
with playalong CD

Christopher Norton

BOOSEY & HAWKES

Boosey & Hawkes Music Publishers Ltd
www.boosey.com

Published by Boosey & Hawkes Music Publishers Ltd
Aldwych House
71–91 Aldwych
London
WC2B 4HN

www.boosey.com

ISMN 979-0-060-11965-1
ISBN 978-0-85162-560-7

First impression 2008

Printed in England by Halstan & Co Ltd, Amersham, Bucks

Piano: Christopher Norton
Tracks: Frank Mizen, Andrew Green
CD Produced by Christopher Norton for CN Productions

CONTENTS

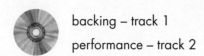

backing – track 1

performance – track 2

1. Colourful

Christopher Norton

With pace ♩=176

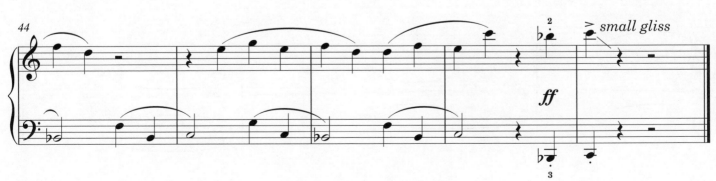

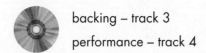

backing – track 3
performance – track 4

2. Moonlit encounter

Christopher Norton

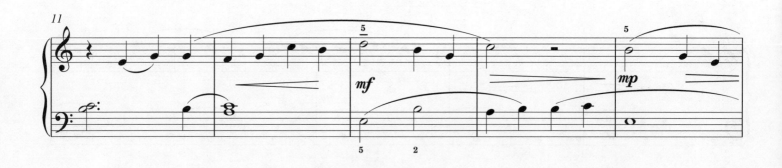

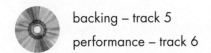

backing – track 5

performance – track 6

3. Excursion

Christopher Norton

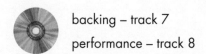

backing – track 7

performance – track 8

4. Heavy load

Christopher Norton

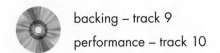
backing – track 9
performance – track 10

5. Sun and sand

Christopher Norton

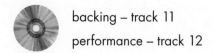

backing – track 11

performance – track 12

6. In the band

Christopher Norton

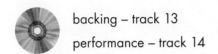

backing – track 13
performance – track 14

7. Beach ball

Christopher Norton

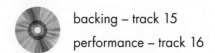

backing – track 15
performance – track 16

8. Jam jar

Christopher Norton

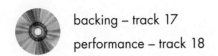

backing – track 17

performance – track 18

9. Esplanade

Christopher Norton

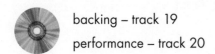

backing – track 19
performance – track 20

10. Tangolita

Christopher Norton

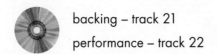

backing – track 21

performance – track 22

11. Light fingered

Christopher Norton

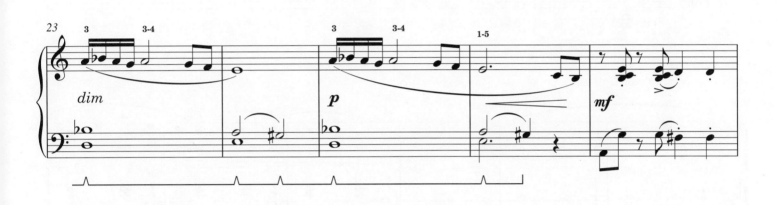

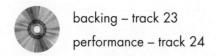

backing – track 23

performance – track 24

12. Sultry night

Christopher Norton

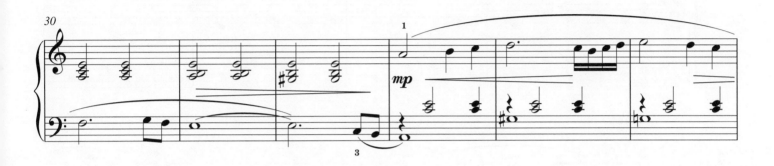

Slowing to the end

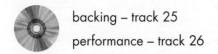

backing – track 25

performance – track 26

13. A gentle ride

Christopher Norton

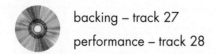

backing – track 27

performance – track 28

14. Bucket and spade

Christopher Norton

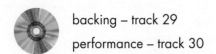
backing – track 29
performance – track 30

15. A bright day

Christopher Norton

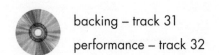
backing – track 31
performance – track 32

16. Island hopper

Christopher Norton

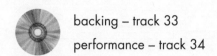

backing – track 33
performance – track 34

17. Stirring the pot

Christopher Norton

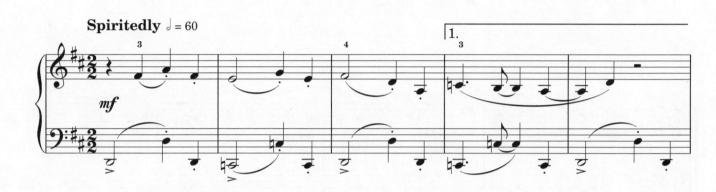

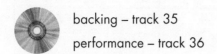

backing – track 35

performance – track 36

18. Warm breeze

Christopher Norton

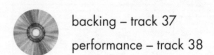

backing – track 37
performance – track 38

19. The rendezvous

Christopher Norton

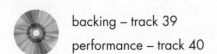

backing – track 39

performance – track 40

20. The parting

Christopher Norton